and then it HAPPENED

~book four~

and then it HAPPENED

~book four~

M & L Wade

Scholastic Canada Ltd.

Toronto New York London Auckland Sydney

Mexico City New Delhi Hong Kong Buenos Aires

Scholastic Canada Ltd.
604 King Street West, Toronto, Ontario M5V 1E1, Canada

Scholastic Inc.
557 Broadway, New York, NY 10012, USA

Scholastic Australia Pty Limited
PO Box 579, Gosford, NSW 2250, Australia

Scholastic New Zealand Limited
Private Bag 94407, Botany, Manukau 2163, New Zealand

Scholastic Children's Books
Euston House, 24 Eversholt Street, London NW1 1DB, UK

www.scholastic.ca

Library and Archives Canada Cataloguing in Publication

Wade, M. (Michael), 1962-
And then it happened / M. & L. Wade.

Originally published: Strathroy, Ont. : Books for Boys,
c2003- ISBN 978-1-4431-1302-1 (bk. 1).--ISBN 978-1-4431-1303-8 (bk. 2).--
ISBN 978-1-4431-1385-4 (bk. 3).--ISBN 978-1-4431-1386-1 (bk. 4)

I. Wade, L. (Laura), 1965- II. Title.

PS8595.A348A64 2011   jC813'.6   C2011-901846-2

7 6 5 4   Printed in Canada   121   14 15 16 17

MIX
Paper from
responsible sources
FSC® C004071

To Chloë, the best companion ever

Table of Contents

Chapter 1 Cheating 1

Chapter 2 The Good Deed 6

Chapter 3 The Scene of the Crime 11

Chapter 4 Butcher's Surprise 19

Chapter 5 The Christmas Present 26

Chapter 6 Hockey Fight in Canada 35

Chapter 7 Lover's Leap 43

Chapter 8 The Day Our Teacher Killed the
        Easter Bunny 59

Chapter 9 Archie's Bad Day 53

Chapter 10 Dog Days of Summer 58

Chapter 11 Toilet Training 63

Chapter 12 The Gas Thief 72

Chapter 13 The Kidnapping 78

Chapter 1
Cheating

It was Friday afternoon and my friends and I were looking forward to a perfect weekend until our teacher announced that our class would be having a major English test on Monday. We let out a collective groan: our weekend was ruined.

"Don't worry about it, guys," Gordon said happily on the way home from school. "I have a plan. We're going to get an A+ on our test, and we're not going to waste time studying on the weekend." He grinned at Paulo and me, and I was immediately suspicious.

"How?" I asked. "You know English isn't my best subject."

Gordon's plan was simple. "The test is Monday afternoon, right? Well, we'll just ride our bikes over to my place for lunch and we'll stay there for the afternoon. We can hang out and watch TV or play computer games. But we'll tell the teacher that, on the way back to school after lunch, one of the tires on my bike got a flat. By the time we walked the bike back to my house, fixed the tire and rode back to school, it was too late. School was already over."

"Not bad," said Paulo. "It just might work."

"Of course it will work," said Gordon.

"You said we'd get an A+," I reminded Gordon. "How are we going to do that if we don't write the test?"

"Easy. On Monday night, we'll phone someone from our class and ask him what was on the test. Then we'll know what to study."

Once again, I had to hand it to Gordon. His plan sounded great.

*　　　*　　　*

Monday came, and at lunch time we made sure Mrs. Hoagsbrith saw the three of us leaving the classroom together.

"We're going to my place for lunch," said Gordon.

"And to do some last-minute reviewing for the big test," added Paulo. Mrs. Hoagsbrith seemed pleased. Our plan was working. So far, so good.

We spent an enjoyable afternoon at Gordon's house, and at twenty minutes to four, the three of us rushed back to school and breathlessly told Mrs. Hoagsbrith about the flat tire and why we were late for school and how sorry we were.

Our teacher looked at us for a long minute, and then she surprised us by saying, "I see. Well, you boys can write the test first thing tomorrow morning. Don't worry about missing it today. Have a good evening, boys."

We left the classroom in stunned, happy silence.

"It worked," I said. "It actually worked!"

"Of course it worked," said Gordon coolly.

That night we phoned a kid from our class who was only too happy to tell us what was on the test. Gordon,

Paulo and I memorized the answers. I couldn't wait to write the test the next day and get an A+!

The next morning, Gordon, Paulo and I were each handed a copy of the test, and then Mrs. Hoagsbrith surprised us by saying that we would be writing it in separate rooms.

"Paulo will go to the library to be supervised by the librarian. Gordon is to go to the office to be supervised by the vice-principal, and you will stay here," she said, pointing to me.

Mrs. Hoagsbrith was separating us! How dare she?! What did she think we were going to do? Cheat? How insulting!

I walked to the table at the back of the room while Gordon and Paulo headed off down the hall. I turned to the first page of the test and read the questions. This was easy! I knew all the answers and quickly filled them in. *A+, here I come,* I thought. My parents would be so proud when they saw my mark that they'd probably buy me something special to celebrate. I smiled as I thought of Gordon and Paulo filling in all the correct answers, too.

I quickly finished the first page and turned to the last page of the test. There was only one question on it, and it was worth seventy-five percent of my mark. It was a simple enough question, but I froze when I saw it, and I knew that Mrs. Hoagsbrith had caught us red-handed.

Sitting in separate rooms, there was no way that all three of us could possibly guess the same answer!

-2-

English Test

75

Which tire on Gordon's bike was flat:
the front one or the back one?

Chapter 2

The Good Deed

It was a hot September afternoon and school was out for the day. Gordon, Paulo and I were walking to my house to watch some TV. Just as we reached my driveway, my neighbour, Mr. Butterworth, came running from his backyard, calling out to us.

"Hey, boys! Come here, quick. I need some help."

We followed him into his backyard to see what the problem was. His four-year-old granddaughter was in the backyard looking up at the top of a tall tree. Perched on the highest branch was a small grey kitten.

"It's been up there all day," explained Mr. Butterworth. "I'm afraid the poor thing'll get weak and fall out."

I looked at his granddaughter's tear-stained face, and then back to the kitten clinging fearfully to the branch.

"My ladder isn't nearly long enough to reach it. Could one of you boys climb up there and bring it down?"

"Please save Fluffy for me!" begged the little girl.

Gordon, Paulo and I carefully looked at the tree and then at each other. Although the tree was very tall, it was also very thin.

"Mr. Butterworth," I said. "We'd love to save Fluffy, but that tree is too thin to climb. We couldn't get more than halfway up without the branches snapping off. We'd fall, and the kitten would get killed."

"I was afraid you'd say that, but Amy wanted me to try." He looked at his granddaughter. We could all hear the kitten crying and knew that it was doomed. Suddenly Gordon brightened. He turned to Mr. Butterworth.

"I've got an idea!" he exclaimed. "Quick! Get some rope. I'll bet if we toss the rope over the top of the tree, the four of us could probably bend the branch down low

7

enough for the kitten to jump off."

Mr. Butterworth hurried into his garage and came out a few seconds later with a large coil of rope. Gordon climbed partway up the tree with the coil over his shoulder, and when he couldn't go any further, he tossed the rope up as hard as he could. It sailed over the branch just below the terrified kitten. Perfect!

Gordon quickly climbed down. Mr. Butterworth, Paulo and I grabbed the end of the rope and began to pull. Gordon's plan worked! The top of the tree began to bend gently downward and soon the branch with the frightened kitten was almost within reach. Mr. Butterworth's granddaughter came forward, arms outstretched, to collect Fluffy and then it happened. With a sharp cracking sound, the rope snapped! The top of the tree flew up, and the poor kitten was catapulted out of sight! There were five loud gasps of horror as we stood there, too stunned to move. Gordon was the first to react, rushing off in the direction the kitten had flown. We followed him through backyards and over fences with Mr. Butterworth and his granddaughter trailing more slowly behind us. About seven houses away, we burst into a backyard and skidded to a stop in front of the local chief of police. He was wearing a bathing suit and he had just climbed out of his pool. In his hands, completely unharmed, was a very wet, scared grey kitten. He immediately started yelling.

"I should have known it would be you kids! This time you've gone too far — throwing a kitten into a swimming pool! If I hadn't been swimming, the poor thing would've drowned! You three are in big trouble! I'm going to . . ." His words died away as Mr. Butterworth burst into the yard, followed by his four-year-old granddaughter, who immediately ran up to the police chief and took the kitten from his hands. Mr. Butterworth quickly explained what had happened and how we had actually been trying to save the kitten, not drown it. The police chief turned red and muttered an apology to Gordon, Paulo and me. Mr. Butterworth's granddaughter hugged us until we begged her to let us go. Mr. Butterworth shook our hands and thanked us over and over. The chief of police looked at my friends and me suspiciously, and I guess I couldn't blame him for not entirely believing Mr. Butterworth's story. I was just relieved to be saved from another trip to the police station.

Chapter 3

The Scene of the Crime

Don't you hate it when bad things happen to good kids? It was Halloween day and Gordon, Paulo and I were at the police station awaiting our parents' arrival. I have begun to notice that adults don't have much of a sense of humour, and the police have none at all. Somehow, what we thought would be a harmless little Halloween prank had gotten a lot of people very mad at us.

When the phone rang at six o'clock this morning and Gordon asked me to meet him and Paulo early in

11

the schoolyard, I should have been suspicious and just hung up, but I was curious, too. So at 7:30 I slipped out of the house when my parents weren't looking and headed toward school. Halfway there, I met up with Gordon and Paulo.

"What's up?" I asked. Gordon wasn't carrying a backpack, but his jacket pocket bulged mysteriously.

"Nothing," said Gordon innocently. "Just a great plan to get a day off school. Maybe two days."

I looked at Paulo, who shrugged his shoulders as if to say, *I don't know. He wouldn't tell me, either.*

When we arrived at school, Gordon marched across the playground and onto the tarmac. He stopped beside a portable classroom and pulled a piece of chalk and some dollar-store caution tape out of his pocket. From another pocket he produced several packets of ketchup. He handed the caution tape and ketchup to Paulo and gave me the chalk.

"Now," he said, lying down on the pavement. "Trace my body with the chalk, just like they do on TV, but stop when you get to my head." I did as I was told, wondering why I had to stop at his head. Maybe so no one would recognize him, I thought.

When I was finished, Gordon got up and moved several feet away and lied down again. "Now trace my head," he said. I took the yellow chalk and outlined his head.

"Now for the finishing touch," Gordon announced, tearing open the packets of ketchup and squeezing out the contents. He spread ketchup around the head and shoulder areas of the two outlines and then squeezed some more around to make it look like a grizzly crime scene. Next came the caution tape. Gordon squared off the area with the yellow tape and then stood back to look at his handiwork.

"It's perfect!" he said, satisfied.

"If by 'perfect' you mean it looks like some kid had his head ripped off here, you're right," said Paulo.

"Exactly," said Gordon. "They can't let us stay in school today if a horrible crime took place here last night. This should be good for at least one day off, if not two." Gordon had always said that Halloween should be a national holiday, like Christmas. Everyone should get the day off in order to celebrate Halloween in their own way. To Gordon, the fact that Halloween wasn't a national holiday was proof that adults just have no sense of humour.

We walked around the block a couple of times while we waited for kids to arrive at school. As we rounded the block for the third time, we were pleased to see a small group of students gathered around our "crime scene." We jogged over to join them.

All the kids just stood there, taking in the scene before them in stunned silence. More kids arrived and joined the growing group beside the portable. There's nothing like a kid with his head torn off to draw a large crowd. A few minutes later, a teacher made her way through the crowd, anxious to see what had captured everyone's attention. The crowd silently parted to let the teacher through. When she saw the scene, she let out a piercing scream. Several more teachers rushed over, and in a minute, our principal, Mr. Evans, lumbered across the schoolyard.

He stared at our crime scene for a few seconds and

then shouted, "Everyone into their classrooms!"

"Ahhh," sighed Gordon as the crowd broke up and headed into the building. "I love starting the principal's day with panic. I bet we'll be sent home within the hour."

Mr. Evans produced a cell phone from his pocket and quickly dialled 9-1-1. Apparently, the police don't get many calls about headless kids, and the entire force was called in. Within minutes, all four of our town's police cars converged on the site, sirens wailing. The officers leapt out of their cars and raced to the crime scene.

Every kid in the building was lined up at the windows, watching. The chief of police took in the crime scene, and then he turned to Mr. Evans. He obviously hadn't been fooled by our little trick, and he was furious that the principal couldn't tell the difference between a fake crime scene and a real one. Even through the closed windows we could hear him shouting.

"YOU'VE JUST WASTED VALUABLE POLICE TIME ON SOME CHILDISH PRANK! COULDN'T YOU SEE THIS IS A FAKE CRIME SCENE? WHAT KIND OF A SCHOOL ARE YOU RUNNING HERE?

CAN'T YOU CONTROL YOUR STUDENTS BETTER THAN THIS? MAYBE IT'S TIME YOU RESIGNED!"

The principal turned and glared menacingly at the school, scanning the windows. Then he and the police officers marched toward the building.

"Uh-oh," whispered Gordon. "Here they come." Every kid turned and scrambled to their seat. We could hear yelling as soon as they entered the building. The police and principal were going from classroom to classroom searching for the culprits. It was getting hard to breathe, and sweat trickled down my back.

They finally got to our classroom and burst through the door. The chief of police didn't waste any time.

"We've been in every class in the building, and no one knows anything about that fake crime scene. I'm guessing that no one in here knows anything, either," he said sarcastically.

Every head in the class shook back and forth, but none so vigorously as guilty Gordon's, and then it happened. As Gordon emphatically shook his head in a show of innocence, I noticed a yellow chalk mark on his left ear.

At that same moment, the chief of police saw the chalk mark, too, and he lunged at Gordon, picking him up by the front of his shirt and lifting him out of his desk with a force that teachers could only dream of.

"YOU!" he demanded. "HOW DO YOU EXPLAIN THIS YELLOW CHALK MARK ON YOUR EAR?"

The police didn't even wait to hear Gordon's weak excuses. He was hauled out of class and deposited into the back of a police car. Just as I was thinking that Paulo and I might escape capture, our ever-helpful principal said, "Wait a minute. If Gordon Smith is guilty, then I'll bet his two friends were involved, too. After all, the kid couldn't trace himself."

The three of us were driven to the police station, and while we waited for our parents to arrive, we received a long lecture about wasting police time and the seriousness of faking a crime scene.

"Are we going to jail?" asked Gordon.

When the police officer said, "No." Gordon almost seemed disappointed.

When I saw the looks on my parents' faces as they

17

came through the door a few minutes later, jail suddenly didn't seem like such a bad idea. I knew that the three of us were in major trouble.

At home, my parents yelled at me for what seemed like hours. They told me how disappointed they were in me and asked how we could have done such a thing.

"I don't know," I mumbled at the floor. "I guess we just lost our heads." I knew the second it was out of my mouth that I shouldn't have said it, but I just couldn't help myself.

In the end, I was glad to escape to my room. I was suspended from school for three days, which wasn't really so bad, but Gordon, Paulo and I were grounded for all three days, which meant that we wouldn't be going trick-or-treating. For the third year in a row, there was to be no Halloween candy for any of us.

Four days later, on our way to school, Gordon said, "If only Halloween were a national holiday like it should be, these sorts of things wouldn't happen."

Paulo and I nodded in agreement and we silently walked on.

Chapter 4

Butcher's Surprise

Kids are sometimes scared by what is known as "the boogeyman," but not in our town. What scared kids in our town was the *booger*man. Unlike the boogeyman, the boogerman was *real*, and every kid had seen him. He was our town's new butcher.

I remember the first time I saw the boogerman. We were at the butcher shop and my mother had just placed an order for some hamburger meat. Then she turned down an aisle and shopped while she waited for the order to be filled, and then it happened. I watched in surprise as the new butcher put his finger into his nose and gave it a good solid pick. He then reached into the hamburger tray with his bare hands and started weighing out our meat. I stood there, rooted to the spot in horror. I couldn't believe it! It was like I had just seen a ghost. In fact, I had just seen the *boogerman!*

On the ride home, I was faced with a dilemma. Should I tell my mother what I had just seen? Would she believe me? In the end, I decided that if I told her, she would probably turn the car around, go back to the butcher shop and complain. The butcher would of course deny it, and my mother would have to decide whom to believe — her kid, who was always in some sort of trouble, or a professional butcher. She would probably believe the butcher, and I would be in trouble for making up lies about him, so I decided to keep my mouth shut.

At home, I took an uncharacteristic interest as my mother prepared dinner. She made four hamburger patties — one for her, one for my dad, one for my sister and one for me. I closed my eyes and hoped that my sister got the one with the secret ingredient.

When dinner was served, I immediately took the meat out of my bun and examined it closely for clues. Where could it be hiding?

"Quit playing with your food!" my father barked at me, with a mouthful of burger. "You're not two years old!" I watched him swallow his food, now hoping it was in *his* hamburger. I put my burger back together and covered it generously with mustard and ketchup, hoping to disguise any bad surprises.

That night I phoned my friend Gordon and told him about the new butcher. Word quickly spread to all the other kids to be on the lookout for the boogerman.

As the days passed, more and more kids reported boogerman sightings.

"It was gross," one kid grumbled. "When he thought no one was looking, I saw him pick away as he made our sausages!"

Not one kid in town tattled on the boogerman. What would be the point? The adults wouldn't believe it, and the butcher was smart enough to conceal his nasty habit from them. He picked away shamelessly, however, when he thought only a kid was watching. What could we do about the boogerman? Even Gordon was stumped. Some kids became vegetarians. Others pretended not to be hungry. We all started losing weight.

One evening while I ate my meatless dinner, my mother announced, "Oh, good news! That nice new butcher has started making school lunches for kids. He calls them 'Butcher's Surprise Sandwiches.' Isn't that cute? I've already ordered a week's worth and told your friends' moms. Think of the time we'll save if we don't have to make your lunches anymore." She beamed with delight.

The next day at lunch time, Gordon, Paulo and I and at least a dozen other kids stared glumly at our Butcher's Surprise Sandwiches.

"Butcher's Surprise!" Gordon muttered. "We all know what the surprise is."

None of us ate our lunches, and by afternoon recess, we were starving. Gordon gathered all the kids who had Butcher's Surprise Sandwiches for lunch and said, "I think I have a plan that'll get rid of the Boogerman. The only problem is, someone might get hurt, or maybe even killed."

Not one of us cared about getting hurt or even killed. We just wanted to get rid of the boogerman.

"I have a disposable camera at home," continued Gordon. "There's one shot left on it. If we can catch the boogerman in action, we'll have proof, and the adults will *have* to believe us."

"But if he catches us, he'll kill us," said Paulo.

"Then we won't let him catch us," replied Gordon. He told us the rest of his plan, and we all agreed it was worth a try.

Half an hour after school let out, we all met again around the corner from the butcher shop. When Gordon arrived with his camera, the other kids got into position with their bikes, and Gordon, Paulo and I headed toward the butcher shop. We took a deep breath and entered the boogerman's lair. He was alone. *Perfect!*

Spotting us, the boogerman laughed and said, "How did you boys enjoy your Butcher's Surprise Sandwiches?" We let the boogerman laugh until he finally asked us for our order.

"One kilogram of hamburger," Gordon said calmly.

"My specialty," chuckled the boogerman, and with that, he reached into his nose. Quick as a cat, Gordon pulled out his camera and snapped the boogerman's picture, catching him in the act.

"Run for it!" Gordon yelled. Fortunately, Paulo and I had been friends with Gordon for many years and we were used to "running for it." We could only hope the other kids were ready, too.

We turned and stampeded for the door with the boogerman hot on our heels. Running up the street, I turned and saw the boogerman quickly gaining on us. A classmate on a bike suddenly pulled up beside us and Gordon handed him the camera.

"GO! GO!" shouted Gordon. "Don't let him catch you!" The kid needed no advice and pedalled furiously away. The boogerman ran after him, no longer concerned about Gordon, Paulo and me. Other kids suddenly appeared on their bikes, cutting in and out in front of the boogerman, slowing him down until he finally gave up the chase.

We had the film developed and an hour later the evidence was clear. There, in living colour for the whole world to see, was the butcher with his finger deep in his nose.

Riding past the butcher shop on our way home with our evidence, we were surprised and delighted to see a sign in the window that read "Out of Business."

Gordon's plan had worked. We had rid the town of the boogerman.

Chapter 5

The Christmas Present

It was the week before Christmas and the weather had turned very cold. The lake froze over, making it ideal for skating and playing hockey, and the toboggan hills were busy all day Saturday and Sunday and every evening. At school, however, it was a completely different story. There were large mounds of snow created by the snowplow that cleared the playground every morning, but of course we were not allowed to play on them. Each day, our principal, Mr. Evans, got on the PA system and warned us to stay off the hills at recess. And naturally, any icy patches on the playground were strictly off-limits, too. That left us with nothing to do at recess but stand around and shiver. It was probably because of our boredom that we noticed that the teachers who roamed around the playground on yard duty looked even colder than we felt.

"Looks like the teachers are suffering, too," I said, slightly glad that they were sharing in our misery for once.

"Yeah," said Paulo. "Look at the grade eight teacher. He doesn't even have boots on. And look at Mrs. H. I guess she forgot her gloves."

Our teacher was walking around the yard with her hands stuffed into the pockets of a large coat. A trail of little kids followed her.

When the bell rang and we finally got back into our warm classrooms, I noticed Mrs. Hoagsbrith blowing on her hands to warm them up.

"Forget your gloves, Mrs. H.?" asked Gordon.

"No. I must have misplaced them," she said. "I'm sure they'll turn up."

But the next day, Mrs. Hoagsbrith was still wandering

around the yard with her hands in her pockets.

"I guess her gloves haven't turned up yet," Gordon commented.

"What?" said Paulo. "Whose gloves?"

"Mrs. H.'s," Gordon replied. "She said she lost hers. Hey, you know how some of the kids in our class said they're getting the teacher a present for Christmas? Well, how about if we chip in and get her a new pair of gloves? You know, to kind of make up for some of the things we've done to the poor lady."

Paulo and I thought that was a great idea. Gordon's family was going Christmas shopping at the mall that night, and we decided to ask our parents if we could go along with them.

When I told my parents that I wanted to go shopping for my teacher, they were pleasantly surprised. They agreed that I could go shopping with Gordon's family and my dad dropped me off at his house right after dinner. Paulo was just ringing the Smith's doorbell as I got out of the car.

Once we got to the mall, Gordon's family decided to

split up so that what they bought for each other would be a surprise. His parents went one way, his sisters went another way, and Gordon, Paulo and I went to the department store to look for gloves. We had been told to meet at the food court in one hour.

The mall was crowded with Christmas shoppers, and we had to wait for 10 minutes before the saleslady could help us.

"We need a warm pair of gloves," I told the woman behind the counter.

"They're for our teacher," added Paulo. The woman pulled out several pairs and we picked out a nice fur-lined pair in black.

"What size does your teacher wear?" the saleslady asked.

"We don't know," said Gordon. "But she sort of looks like you. What size do you wear?"

The saleslady tried on several sizes and found the one that fit her best. "Would you like them gift-wrapped? It doesn't cost anything extra."

We paid for the gloves and left the store with a

beautifully wrapped present. We had some extra time, so we decided to try and find Gordon's parents and snoop to see what they were buying Gordon for Christmas.

It didn't take long to find them. They were in the same store where we had bought the gloves. We were too late to snoop, though. They had several bags with them and we could see boxes all wrapped up in paper just like ours.

We met Gordon's sisters in the food court, and Mr. Smith treated everyone to hot chocolate. Then we loaded our gifts into the back of the minivan and everyone piled in for the ride home.

"Thanks for the ride and the hot chocolate," I said as I got out at my house. "Don't forget the present tomorrow, Gordon." I added.

The next morning, Gordon appeared at school with the gift and a nice Christmas card. He had written a note to the teacher inside and told Paulo and me to sign it. Then we would give it to the teacher together. I read what Gordon had written.

Dear Mrs. Hoagsbrith,

We hope you like the present we bought you.
We noticed you weren't wearing any the other
day and thought you could use a new pair. The
saleslady tried them on to make sure they fit.
Merry Christmas

The teacher's desk was piled high with gifts from students. We added ours to the pile and sat down. Mrs. Hoagsbrith thanked everyone and said that she would open the gifts at home. I guess she didn't want the kids who didn't get her a present to feel bad. I was feeling very good about our gift and, even better, that today was the last day of school before Christmas vacation started.

*   *   *

At my house, we always open up our presents on Christmas Eve. I think that's so my parents can sleep in on Christmas Day without my sister and me bugging them at the crack of dawn to get up. I got a bunch of really neat stuff, and for the first time since I can remember, not one single box contained underwear.

I woke up early the next morning and looked at all my stuff under the tree. No one was awake yet at my house, so I decided that it would be fun to go over to Gordon's house to see what he got for Christmas. I quickly got dressed, put on my coat and boots, and quietly closed the door behind me.

When I arrived at the Smith's house, they were only halfway through opening up their gifts. Gordon has four sisters, so it takes a long time to open all those presents. Gordon's mother insists that the presents be handed out one at a time by the youngest daughter. Gordon's mother got me a glass of eggnog and a cinnamon bun for breakfast, and the family went back to opening presents. I recognized the wrapping paper on several gifts. They came from the same department store where we had bought Mrs. Hoagsbrith's gloves. I hoped she liked them.

"Now these next gifts are all the same," said Mrs. Smith. "So you should open them together." Everyone tore the paper off the boxes at the same time. All of the boxes contained underwear. I laughed as Gordon held up a new pair of boxer shorts, and then it happened.

"Hey," said Gordon's youngest sister. "Mine's not the same. I didn't get underpants. I got these nice gloves!" She held up a pair of fur-lined black gloves.

"Hey," exclaimed Gordon. "Those look just like the gloves that we bought for . . . OH, MY GOSH! THOSE ARE MY TEACHER'S GLOVES!"

"But then what's in the box we gave her?" I asked, and then it hit me. Gordon and I stared at each other open-mouthed. "Gordon!" I hissed. "You must have gotten the boxes mixed up! WE GAVE OUR TEACHER *UNDERWEAR* FOR CHRISTMAS!"

Gordon's dad laughed out loud, and I thought I saw a smile on Mrs. Smith's face, too. His sisters began to giggle, and Gordon himself burst out laughing.

"It's not funny!" I said. "Don't you remember what you wrote on the card? We said, 'We noticed you weren't wearing any!' We said, 'The saleslady tried them on!'"

That only made Gordon laugh harder. The entire Smith family was in hysterics. Apparently I was the only one who didn't think that this was funny at all. How would I ever be able to face my teacher again?

Chapter 6

Hockey Fight In Canada

Violence in hockey is a problem in many kids' leagues. The parents in our hockey league put their heads together and came up with a solution that worked quite well at first. Their idea for reducing the violence was to put three parents on each team to give guidance and add maturity to the league. In the beginning, things improved greatly: penalty minutes were reduced and hardly anyone ever needed stitches. Then came the playoffs.

Our team, the Buzzards, was in the finals against a team from a neighbouring town, the Lemmings. All of a sudden, our mature, level-headed, example-setting fathers turned into hard-hitting, competitive, fast-skating demons on the ice. Instead of preaching the importance of sportsmanship, teamwork and fair play, they were yelling, "Check him!", "Hit him!" and "Take him out!" Their play became rougher, too. The fathers on our team were now mixing it up with the dads on the Lemmings. The penalty box was almost constantly occupied with fathers, and it was only Game 1.

The series progressed through six long and bloody games, and now we were ready to face the Lemmings in the seventh deciding match.

The pre-game pep talk was delivered by Gordon's father in the dressing room.

"This is the final game," he began. "And tonight, we will leave this arena as champions! I want to see some real hockey out there. No cowardice! No backing down! Go out there and give 'em h—"

"What about good sportsmanship and fun?" interrupted a voice from the back.

"Who said that?" shouted Gordon's father. "Good sportsmanship is for losers! And winning *is* fun! Now get out there and show 'em what you're made of!"

We headed out of the dressing room and skated onto the ice. The sold-out arena went wild, our fans cheering and blowing bull horns and the Lemmings' fans booing and hissing at us. It looked like both entire towns had turned out for the final game.

The national anthem was played, and then the ref blew the whistle for the game to begin. Paulo skated to centre ice to take the faceoff against the Lemmings' centre — a hulking two-hundred-pound father against a twelve-year-old kid. The puck dropped and Paulo was instantly flattened. The Lemmings' fans roared with delight while our fans booed and called for a penalty. The play continued as Paulo struggled to his feet. By the end of the first period the game was tied 1–1, and we had lost two of our best players to injury.

Holding a bag of ice to his swelling eye, Gordon's father gave us another rousing pep talk in the dressing room. "Men, this is war!" he declared. "We didn't start it, but so help me, we're gonna finish it! If we lose this game, we'll be letting down our entire town, and we'll be a town of losers! Buzzards are not losers!" Gordon's dad had suddenly turned into a drill sergeant.

The second period began and went much like the first. The penalty box was almost always filled with somebody's dad. Fathers tripped, elbowed and smashed each other whenever they could. As bad as things were on the ice, they were worse in the stands. The fans had caught the mood of the game, and they began punching and yelling at each other. Things inside the arena were quickly turning into a riot. Fans were screaming at each other, fathers were yelling at each other, and everyone was shouting at the referees. The only ones not yelling were the kids on the ice. We tried to keep fairness and good sportsmanship in mind while total war raged around us. Our fathers and fans wanted to win, and never mind the rules. When the second period finally ended, the game was tied 2–2.

From the dressing room, we could hear the fans roaring above Mr. Smith's pep talk, which was more like a pep *shout*.

"Men, we're gonna win this game and drive the Lemmings out of this arena and out of our town! They will return home losers and live the rest of their lives in failure and shame!"

Our dads banged their sticks on the ground and chanted, "BUZZ-ARDS! BUZZ-ARDS! BUZZ-ARDS!" The kids on our team stared at each other. We couldn't decide who was worse — the fans or our fathers.

The third period started off amidst the screaming of the fans and the frenzy of our dads. The Lemmings wanted to win as badly as we did, and it was obviously going to be a bloody fight to the finish.

As we neared the final minutes of play, the score was still tied 2–2. Neither goalie was letting anything by him. Everyone knew that whichever team scored the next goal would probably go home the winners.

Suddenly, the puck was passed to Gordon at centre ice. He turned and streaked toward the Lemmings' net with a burst of speed. The Lemmings' defencemen had been caught down at the other end of the ice and they frantically tried to stop Gordon's breakaway. Just as

Gordon raised his stick to shoot, one of the Lemmings reached out with his stick and caught it between Gordon's skates. With a sharp jab, he flipped Gordon into the air with such force that Gordon almost did a complete somersault. With a bone-jarring crunch, Gordon landed on his back, unable to move. Our fans went wild. The ref blew the whistle to stop the play, but it couldn't be heard above the roar in the arena, and then it happened. Gordon's dad saw his son lying unconscious on the ice and went wild. All the fathers on our team threw down their sticks and gloves and paired off with fathers from the other team. It was Buzzard against Lemming everywhere you looked — on the ice and in the stands. In one corner, two referees were even beating each other up. Fans spilled out onto the ice looking for revenge. I saw our town's mayor seize the other town's mayor in a headlock and throw him onto the ice. Grandparents swung their canes and walkers at other grandparents. I even saw our principal, Mr. Evans, slugging it out with a principal from the other town. When I saw our teacher, Mrs. Hoagsbrith, throw a coffee cup at a parent from the other team, I realized, *Yes, this is a hockey town.*

I caught sight of Paulo and the two of us made our way over to where Gordon still lay on the ice.

"Are you OK?" I asked, bending over him. Gordon grinned up at me.

"Sure," he said. "I took a dive. That guy hardly touched me."

Meanwhile, in the arena, things were totally out of control, and I could hear sirens in the distance as the police sped to the site.

"Gordon, look what you've done!" I shouted above the noise. "Your fake dive caused a riot!"

Gordon got to his feet and shouted, "Follow me!" Paulo and I followed him off the ice, dodging bruised and bloody players until we came to a door with a sign on it that read "Maintenance" Gordon entered the unlocked room and quickly found a large switch marked "Lights." He pulled the switch, plunging the arena into total darkness.

The riot was stopped in its tracks. A second later, the dim emergency lights came on, illuminating the exits.

Fans made their way out of the building along with several players who had obviously had enough. The great hockey fight was over.

A few minutes later, after most of the crowd had gone home, Gordon turned the lights back on.

The ice was littered with broken sticks, gloves, helmets, food and clothing. I even saw a pair of false teeth on the blue line.

The game was over, and no one had won. For the first time in the history of our league, it was declared that there were two losers in the playoffs. No one got to take home the big trophy. No team got its picture in the paper. There was no MVP. Our fathers had to agree to stop playing hockey in our league, and our fans were banned from the arena until they took an anger management course. On the plus side, no one was arrested. The kids were allowed to play again the following year, as long as we agreed to forget everything that Gordon's dad and the other fathers had taught us about hockey, and just play the game our own way from now on.

Chapter 7

Lover's Leap

There are some things in life that you just know are wrong. I don't know how my friends and I can be such good kids when our parents and teachers are watching, but when left on our own, Gordon, Paulo and I are drawn to trouble like moths to the flame. And like moths, we sometimes get burnt. Our parents have spent our whole lives teaching us right from wrong, but when we're away from them, we use our own system of telling right from wrong: will we get caught or not? An example of this was a new game that we invented.

Just outside of town (and only a fifteen-minute bike ride from Paulo's farm) is a dead end road where teenagers park their cars and make out. It's called Lover's Lane. During sleepovers at Paulo's house, once we're sure his parents are asleep, the three of us sneak out and ride our bikes over to Lover's Lane to play jokes on the couples in their cars.

Late one night last spring, Gordon, Paulo and I biked over to Lover's Lane and found a lone car parked there. Sneaking up on the car, we quietly counted to three. Then at the same moment we all turned on our powerful flashlights and pressed our faces up against the steamy windows. The interior of the car was flooded in blinding light, and like deer caught in the headlights, the surprised young couple stared in panic at our squished faces. There was a flurry of screaming and yelling as the car took off like a rocket, gravel flying out behind it. Gordon, Paulo and I dove into the ditch, laughing hysterically.

The next week we were allowed to have another sleepover at Paulo's house, and this time we had an even better plan. When Paulo's parents finally turned off their bedroom light, we snuck out and biked to Lover's Lane. We were delighted to discover almost 10 cars parked there. We ditched our bikes and opened a bag that contained Paulo's dad's farm clothes — a pair of coveralls, a hat and work boots. Gordon put on the outfit and Paulo and I stuffed the coveralls full of old newspapers. When we were done, Gordon looked like a very large farmer. For the finishing touch, I untied a pitchfork from my bike and handed it to Gordon. We grinned at each other, and Paulo and I ducked behind the bushes to watch the fun. Gordon stepped into the middle of the crowded parking lot, and with the bright full moon behind him, he yelled in his loudest, deepest voice, "WHERE'S MY DAUGHTER? I WANT TO SEE MY DAUGHTER RIGHT NOW!" He waved the pitchfork about menacingly.

Not one guy wanted to take the chance that his date was this crazy farmer's daughter. In an instant, every engine roared to life and the cars fled down the dirt road, raising a cloud of dust. We laughed hysterically until the last tail lights were out of sight and then pedalled back to Paulo's house to plan our next attack on Lover's Lane.

Two weeks later, we finally got permission for another sleepover. It was midnight when we reached Lover's Lane and there was only one car parked there. We crouched in the ditch to put the final touches on our plan. It was simple. One after the other, Gordon, Paulo and I would run up to the car, leap onto the hood, run over the roof, and down the trunk. We could only imagine what the young couple inside would think as a stampede thundered over their heads!

On the count of three, Gordon took off like a shot and sprinted toward the car. He leapt up onto the hood, and then it happened. As Gordon sprinted onto the roof, we heard a loud tear and Gordon's legs plunged straight down into the car! *The car was a convertible with a soft top!* There was a sudden outburst of screaming and yelling from inside the car while Gordon struggled desperately to pull himself out. Swearing loudly, the angry man inside the car swung at Gordon's legs while Gordon kicked and continued to struggle.

"You little brat! Just wait 'til I'm through with you!" shouted the man as he tried to pull Gordon into the car.

Paulo and I rushed over and grabbed Gordon's arms, creating a human tug-of-war. After several long seconds of struggling and twisting, we heard a tearing sound, and Gordon flew out of the car, minus his pants.

"RUN!" he shouted. We wasted no time in running to the safety of the dark woods. Hiding in the bushes, we heard the car door slam and saw the beam of a flashlight as the irate man searched the woods for us, swearing and threatening what he was going to do to us for destroying his roof and ruining his date. We crouched like frightened rabbits until he finally grew tired of looking for us and returned to his car and drove away. We slowly stood up and walked back to where we had left our bikes in the ditch. Gordon shivered in his underwear as we silently pedalled home.

We agreed that we'd had enough of Lover's Lane. The couples there didn't seem to appreciate our kind of humour. This time had been a really close call, but we'd gotten away with it, or so we thought . . .

*   *   *

On Monday morning, we took our seats as usual in class. Our teacher, Mrs. Hoagsbrith, told us to take out our English books. Gordon opened his desk and was shocked to find his torn pants inside. He looked up and stared open-mouthed into the knowing face of Mrs. Hoagsbrith. Suddenly it became clear to us — our teacher had been the woman in the convertible at Lover's Lane!

Chapter 8

The Day Our Teacher Killed the Easter Bunny

Last Easter, Gordon, Paulo and I saved our Easter baskets and all that kiddy stuff that comes with the candy — you know, the plastic egg shells, the stuffed toys and the crinkly shredded paper that lines the basket. Why our mothers still bother with all those silly decorations I don't know. Six year olds may love it, but at our age our policy is: Fewer Easter decorations; more Easter candy. I guess moms will be moms. If it were left to our dads, they'd probably forget all about Easter until the last minute and then slip us a few dollars and point us to the nearest candy

49

store. But as I was saying, last year we saved all that kiddy stuff because we had a great idea. All we needed now was one dead rabbit.

We began our search for a roadkill rabbit on Monday after school, pedalling our bikes up and down the country roads. After three days of hard searching, we were still empty-handed.

"Geez," Gordon griped. "There's never a dead rabbit around when you want one." But on the fourth day, luck was on our side and we found one. It was a beauty, too. It had been hit by a car but wasn't mangled too badly. We knew better than to bring our dead rabbit home. Any kid caught with a dead rabbit was bound to be asked a million questions by his parents, and no matter what you answered, the rabbit would be taken from you and thrown out. Instead, we stashed our rabbit behind a bush on the edge of the schoolyard, ready for the next day.

The following morning, Gordon, Paulo and I arrived at school early, armed with last year's Easter baskets and decorations, which we hid with our dead rabbit.

I kept my eye on the clock as the school day wore on,

waiting for the moment when Gordon would ask to go to the washroom, and then run outside to put our plan into action. We knew that every day at eleven o'clock, the little kindergarten kids went outside to play on the swings and slide, which was right beside the teachers' parking lot. At ten minutes to eleven, Gordon raised his hand and asked to be excused. Once outside the classroom, he raced silently down the hall and out of the building, glancing over his shoulder to make sure no one was watching. At the same moment, Paulo raised his hand and asked Mrs. Hoagsbrith for help with a complicated math problem. The idea was to keep the teacher busy so she wouldn't notice how long Gordon was gone, or worse, wander past the window and glance out at the schoolyard.

Several minutes passed before Gordon returned. He smiled and gave me the thumbs-up sign as he slid into his seat, picked up his pencil and began his work. At eleven o'clock I looked out of the window and saw the line of kindergarten kids heading toward the playground equipment at the far end of the schoolyard, and then it happened. At one minute past eleven, I heard the first shout, and then came the cries of twenty five-year-olds as they discovered the grizzly scene in the teachers' parking lot. Spread all over the ground around Mrs. Hoagsbrith's car were Easter baskets, stuffed bunnies and plastic eggs, and tucked under the wheel of our teacher's car was our dead rabbit!

As the cries grew louder, our whole class rushed to the window to see what was going on.

"Gee," said Gordon innocently. "It looks like somebody ran over the Easter Bunny!" There was laughter from several of the kids in our class, and Mrs. Hoagsbrith rushed outside to help the kindergarten teacher console the wailing tots.

"Well, I'll bet Mrs. H. will have some explaining to do!" said Gordon cheerfully as he rooted through the teacher's desk. "Hey, look! Here's my old slingshot!"

Chapter 9

Archie's Bad Day

It was a warm spring evening and Gordon and I were over at Paulo's house. His grandmother was visiting from Portugal and tomorrow was her 90th birthday.

"She doesn't seem too happy about turning 90," Gordon remarked as we heard voices coming from inside the house. We stopped and listened as Gordon's grandmother complained about having to spend the whole day by herself on her birthday.

"I didn't come all this way to sit around here alone on my birthday . . . maybe my last birthday!"

"But, Mother," said Paulo's dad. "You know we have to work, and Paulo can't stay home from school."

"It's still not a very nice way to spend my birthday!" she grumbled.

"I don't know what she's complaining about," Paulo told Gordon and me. "I offered to stay home from school, but my parents said 'No.' And we're taking her out to a really fancy restaurant for dinner tomorrow."

Gordon, Paulo and I sat on the back porch drinking Coke and listening to Paulo's grandmother tell off Paulo's parents: how she came all the way from Portugal to be with them on her 90th birthday, how ungrateful they were and how nobody cared about her. On and on she went.

"Is she always this mean?" I asked Paulo.

"No. She doesn't really like my mother, and she's never quite forgiven my dad for moving to Canada, but she's really nice to me."

"Hey! I have an idea that might make her happy!" said Gordon. "Why don't we bring Archie over to keep her company tomorrow?"

Archie was Gordon's pet parrot. He could talk and do tricks, but Archie'd had a disease when he was younger that had caused all of his feathers to permanently fall out. He was a great pet and good company, but he looked a little scary.

"That's a great idea," said Paulo. "She can have fun with Archie, and she won't be alone. Plus, I can say it's my present to her. I didn't buy her anything."

Gordon and I arranged to bring Archie over first thing in the morning.

The next day Gordon and I rode our bikes over to Paulo's house with Archie's cage strapped across Gordon's handlebars. Paulo's parents were already at work, but his grandmother was still in bed.

"She's really going to like this," said Paulo. "But I think we should leave a note explaining about Archie. After all, he does look a little weird."

I don't think Gordon appreciated Paulo calling his parrot weird, but he agreed that a note would be a good idea. Paulo got a piece of paper and wrote:

Dear Grandma,

 I'm sorry you have to spend the day alone.
Please enjoy this surprise for your birthday.
See you after school.

 Love, Paulo

We put Archie on the counter in the kitchen right next to the flowers and chocolates that Paulo's parents had bought for her.

"Be good, Archie," Gordon said as we left. "See you later."

   * * *

At the end of the day, Gordon and I rode the school bus home with Paulo so that Gordon could pick up Archie. We were anxious to see how Paulo's grandmother had enjoyed Archie's company.

When we got near the back door, we heard yelling, and then it happened.

"I wonder what's wrong now?" said Paulo as we entered the house.

"But, Mother," Paulo's dad was saying. "We thought you *loved* chocolate."

"I hate the stuff!" she shouted. "And you know I'm allergic to flowers. What were you thinking? And to think that this could be my last birthday!" Then she caught sight of Gordon, Paulo and me. Her face was suddenly all smiles and she came toward Paulo with her arms outstretched.

"But *you!*" she said to Paulo. "That was a lovely gift you left me. Thank you so much for that little chicken. It was delicious!"

Chapter 10

Dog Days of Summer

or

Fun with Dog Food

It was summer and I had two months of vacation to look forward to. My parents were always telling me that my friends and I have too much time on our hands and that's why we get into so much trouble. I tell *them* that if we had more money in our hands then we could afford to *keep* out of trouble. The reason we get into trouble is because we're always forced to entertain ourselves with so little. Take, for example, Gordon's recent discovery of a new use for dog food.

Gordon's dog, Chopper, loves Woof-Brand dog food,

and Gordon's discovery was pure genius. He found that if you take a handful of Woof-Brand dog food, you can roll it between your hands like playdough until it looks exactly like a glistening, fresh dog dropping! It didn't take very long before we found a very good use for these fake dog droppings. Gordon opened several cans of Woof-Brand and Paulo and I got busy rolling. We made about thirty "dog droppings" and then we put them in a bag which Gordon hid at the back of the fridge.

Early the next morning, Paulo and I biked to Gordon's house. He was waiting for us with the bag in his hands. We pedalled to the park, where everybody likes to take their dogs for a walk. Because it was so early, there were very few people around. Perfect! Gordon, Paulo and I began distributing the "dog droppings" around the park, placing them on walkways, near trees and in the grass, where they glistened in the morning dew. Then we sat on a bench to watch the fun.

Soon, an old lady came walking by with one of those tiny little dogs on a leash. As they came closer to the first "dog dropping," the little dog caught a whiff of Woof-

Brand dog food and started sniffing the ground furiously with its tiny nose. And then it happened. The dog quickly spotted the food and started gobbling up its prize. The old lady glanced down and saw her dog eating what she naturally assumed was real dog poo. She shrieked and yanked her little dog away from the "poo." The dog looked up at her with a puzzled expression on its face, as if to say, "What are you doing? It's just dog food!" When it opened its mouth to show her, the lady looked like she was about to faint! She hauled the little pooch away, muttering something about taking it home to brush its teeth.

Sitting on the nearby bench, Gordon, Paulo and I cracked up.

"Here comes another one!" whispered Paulo excitedly. We watched while another dog, this time much larger, caught the scent of Woof-Brand and began sniffing around until he found the fake dog dropping. He, too, wolfed it down to the dismay of his owner.

"Drop it!" commanded the angry owner. "Bad dog!"

The scene was the same all over the park. Dogs sniffed out the dog food and gobbled it up while their owners looked on, disgusted and angry. Dogs broke free from their owners in their frenzy to find the source of what to them was a wonderful odour — Woof-Brand dog food. All the while, Gordon, Paulo and I watched the scene and laughed 'til our sides ached.

Just when we thought things couldn't get better, a police car pulled into the parking lot, its siren blaring. Apparently someone had reported that dogs in the park were going crazy and running wild, and the police showed up to see for themselves. Then things really got interesting when a van from the local news arrived to capture the excitement on camera.

"This is great!" exclaimed Gordon. "This is gonna be on the news!"

At six o'clock that night, we tuned into the local news and listened while a man reported the strange happenings in the park that morning. He said that dogs were misbehaving and running wild and eating dog droppings. I laughed out loud. The reporter actually said "dog droppings" right on the news! Dog owners were advised to keep a close eye on their pets when they walked them in the park.

Gordon's plan had worked even better than we had expected. *This summer's going to be great*, I thought and sighed happily.

Chapter 11

Toilet Training

With the exception of flushing the occasional dead goldfish, most people think toilets are good for only one thing — going to the bathroom. Little kids master toilet training by the age of two or three, and they never really give toilets much thought after that, but Gordon has never stopped thinking about toilets, or to be more specific, the *fun* you can have with toilets. It was Gordon who taught us that if you pour Jell-O powder into a toilet and swish it around, it will turn into real Jell-O. Gordon actually did this at school when he was in kindergarten. It was

December and the whole school was decorated for Christmas. Gordon poured red and green Jell-O into all of the toilets and let it set overnight. When he got caught, he explained to the principal that he had only wanted to make the bathrooms look more Christmassy. The principal made Gordon clean out all of the toilets and told him he was going to keep an eye on him. Six years later, the principal's eye has never left Gordon.

As the years passed, Gordon added many more tricks to his toilet arsenal, all of which came in very handy last year at summer camp. Camp Outback — or Camp *Outhouse*, as the kids all called it — was really a great place, despite having no flush toilets. Gordon, Paulo and I had been looking forward to camp for weeks and when the big day finally arrived, we boarded the bus with great anticipation. When we arrived at Camp Outhouse, we piled off the bus and were met by the head counsellor, a nice guy named Dave. Dave led us to our cabins, pointing out all of the new things along the way, like the new slide at the lake, the new canoes and, finally (he saved the best for last), the new washroom with real flush toilets! The kids cheered and shouted. As I said, most people don't give toilets a second thought, but when you and a hundred other guys are forced to use outhouses for two straight weeks, things can get pretty smelly. We all crowded into the washroom to admire the gleaming new white toilets with black seats. Gordon turned to Paulo and me with a glint in his eye. *Here we go again,* I thought.

"Guys, this is going to be our best year at camp yet," said Gordon. "One hundred kids, a row of shiny new toilets and no parents or teachers for miles!"

"What are you going to do?" I asked suspiciously.

"You'll see," was all Gordon would say.

*   *   *

We had been at camp a few days when a large box arrived in the mail for Gordon.

"What'd you get?" I asked anxiously, peering over Gordon's shoulder as he tore open the package. Secretly, I hoped his parents had sent us something good to eat, but when I looked into the box, I was greatly disappointed. Inside were a couple of pens and a roll of plastic food wrap.

"It's from my sister," explained Gordon. "I asked her to send this stuff, and it's *exactly* what we need. Boys, let the toilet training begin."

Early the next morning, I saw Gordon quietly sneaking out of the cabin at the crack of dawn, the roll of plastic food wrap tucked under his arm. Ten minutes later he was back in his bunk, pretending to be asleep. I chuckled to myself and waited for the fun to begin.

About half an hour later the camp came to life, and kids rolled out of their bunks and headed off toward the new washroom. Within thirty seconds, we could hear yelling and cursing as one camper after another discovered that all of the new toilet bowls had been neatly covered in plastic wrap. People are always telling us to forgive and forget, but it's hard to turn the other cheek when it's pressed up against plastic wrap and you just went to the bathroom all over yourself. Angry campers swore and shook their fists as they headed off to the showers to get cleaned up.

"Nicely done," said Paulo when the three of us were alone.

"Yeah, you sure got those kids good," I added.

"That was nothing," said Gordon. "Wait until you see what I've planned next."

Things were quiet for the next couple of days at camp, but on the third day, kids started noticing a strange rash on their butts. It didn't itch or sting, but it was a very odd colour — blue. Nobody was brave enough to visit the camp nurse (I mean, who wants to drop their shorts and have their butt examined?), but as more and more campers came down with the mysterious ailment that we now called "blue butt," our cabin counsellor forced one poor kid to go to the nurse's office. After a careful (and embarrassing) examination, the nurse discovered that the rash was actually pen ink. The head counsellor, who had blue butt himself, traced the source of the ink to the toilet seats in the new washroom. He hit the roof and declared that until the person who had pulled these pranks either confessed or was caught, he was locking the new washroom and we would be all be forced to use the outhouses again.

"Not a problem," I whispered to Paulo. "Gordon's

toilet tricks have got me so nervous, I haven't used the new washroom since we arrived at camp anyway."

Naturally, Gordon had no intention of confessing, and he was such an expert at pulling pranks that there was no way he was going to be caught, especially not by some overgrown Boy Scout playing head counsellor.

"I guess this puts an end to your toilet tricks," Paulo said to Gordon. "With no one using the new washroom, there's no one to pull pranks on." But Paulo was wrong.

The next day we discovered that all of the counsellors had keys to the new washroom. Only us kids had to use the smelly old outhouses. As we stood in line waiting to go, we watched the counsellors unlock the washroom and let themselves in.

"That's hardly fair," grumbled the kid in line ahead of me. "I mean, how do we know the person pulling those pranks was even a kid? It might have been a counsellor."
"I'll bet it *was* one of the counsellors," said Gordon. "And I can prove it. I'll bet the pranks don't stop just because we're not allowed in the washroom anymore. If they continue, we'll know it was one of them." Geez, Gordon had nerve.

That same night Paulo and I were awakened by Gordon, who whispered for us to meet him outside. We quickly threw on some clothes, slid into our shoes and quietly left the cabin.

"What's up?" I whispered when I caught up to Gordon.

"I need your help," said Gordon as we headed down the path to the new washroom. "I'm gonna make it look like one of the counsellors has been pulling these pranks all along."

"How?" I demanded.

"My secret weapon," said Gordon, pulling an empty pillowcase from his pocket.

"What's that for?" I asked.

"You'll see," he replied.

"And how are you going to get into the washroom without a key?" I added.

"That's where you come in handy," said Gordon. "You're going to boost me up to the window, and I'm going to crawl through. Then I'll stand on the sink and climb back out."

"I still don't get it," I said. "What's the joke?"

"You'll see," said Gordon again.

We arrived at the washroom, and Paulo and I boosted Gordon up and into the open window. A few minutes went by, and then the bulging pillowcase was tossed back out of the open window. A minute later, Gordon climbed out and dropped to the ground. I picked up the pillowcase and looked inside. It was filled with toilet paper.

Early the next morning, the entire cabin was once again awakened by shouting and swearing coming from the new washroom. This time, however, it wasn't kids who were yelling: it was the counsellors. Campers jumped out of their bunks and raced up the path to see what the commotion was all about.

"Where's the toilet paper?" we heard someone shout. It sounded like Dave, the head counsellor.

"There's none in this stall, either!" yelled another voice.

"Or in mine!" hollered an angry counsellor. "I'm gonna kill the kid who stole all the toilet paper!" And then it happened. A hush fell over the washroom as it dawned on the counsellors that kids were no longer allowed in the new washroom and therefore the prankster had to be one of *them*.

"THAT'S IT!" roared the head counsellor. "EVERYONE OUT!" One by one, the counsellors came out of the washroom. "Now hand over your keys!" he ordered. Keys were dropped into Dave's open hand. Next, the head counsellor ordered a search of the entire campground for the missing toilet paper. It was soon found in the bushes outside one of the counsellor's cabins.

"Aha!" cried the head counsellor in triumph. "I think we've found the guilty party."

Paulo and I just stared at Gordon in amazement. Not only had he pulled a great prank on the counsellors, but he'd made it look like one of *them* had stolen all of the toilet paper.

Thanks to Gordon, from that day on, the counsellors were forced to line up at the outhouse, and only the campers were allowed to use the new washroom.

Chapter 12

The Gas Thief

Summer was almost over and Gordon's Uncle Ivan had rented a fancy motor home. He parked the RV in a campground and Paulo, Gordon and I were invited to go visit him for one week. We had a great time swimming in the lake, fishing, riding our bikes up and down the dirt roads, and, when it rained, we watched movies inside the RV. There was a camp store that sold ice cream cones, chips and pop, so we were never without a steady supply of snacks. Our week with Gordon's uncle was flying by and soon it would be time for us to go home. On the last night of our visit, just as we were sitting down to dinner, the manager of the campground knocked on our door.

"It looks like we've got a gas thief on the loose," he told Uncle Ivan. "Someone's been going around after dark and siphoning gas out of people's tanks. He drained five trailers last night alone. The police are going to stay in my RV tonight and try to catch the guy. If you hear anything suspicious after dark, honk your horn and turn on your headlights. The police will come by and investigate."

Gordon, never one to miss an opportunity for adventure or to make money, listened carefully to every word the campground manager said.

"Is there a reward for catching the guy?" he asked eagerly.

"Of course," said the manager. "Nobody'll want to stay here if there's a gas thief on the loose. We're offering a $250.00 reward to anyone who helps the police catch him."

Gordon's eyes lit up when he heard about the reward. After dinner, as we sat around the campfire, Gordon talked about all the things we could buy with $250.00.

"But we have to help the police catch the thief," I

reminded him. "And tonight's our last night here."

"Yeah. Forget it, Gordon," added Paulo, but Gordon couldn't forget it. His mind was busy thinking up ways to help catch the thief.

All of a sudden, Gordon rose from his chair and went into the RV. He came out a few seconds later carrying a screwdriver and grinning.

"Guys," he announced. "I think I have the perfect way to catch any thief who tries to steal our gas."

"How?" Paulo and I asked together.

"Oh, you'll see," said Gordon, grinning. "It's a surprise." He disappeared around the other side of the trailer and returned a few minutes later looking pleased with himself.

We enjoyed our last campfire of the week and ate an entire bag of marshmallows toasted over the coals. When it was finally time to go to bed, Gordon said, "Don't get undressed. We should all sleep in our clothes so we can be ready to catch the gas thief." He stretched out on top of the covers with his shoes still on and promptly went to sleep. Paulo and I fell asleep almost as quickly.

I was sound asleep when something woke me in the middle of the night. I strained in the darkness to identify the faint rustling noise. With my head next to the screen, I could hear the sound of soft footsteps getting closer to our RV. The footsteps stopped and I held my breath. Someone was on the other side of the trailer's thin metal wall. I could hear a faint scraping sound as the gas cap was unscrewed. I peered out of the tiny window and saw the outline of a man with a rubber hose raised to his lips. I was so close I could have reached out and touched the thief!

I was just about to yell out and wake the others, and then it happened. A hand was clamped over my mouth!

"Shhh." It was Gordon. He kept his hand over my mouth as we watched the thief suck on the siphon hose to draw up the gas.

Suddenly the thief threw down the hose and began spitting and retching. He held his throat and rolled around on the ground.

"Come on!" yelled Gordon. Uncle Ivan and Paulo jumped out of their beds in surprise.

"Turn on the lights!" shouted Gordon. "Honk the horn, Uncle Ivan! It's the gas thief!"

Gordon, Paulo and I rushed out of the trailer in time to see the thief staggering off into the bushes.

"DON'T LET HIM GET AWAY!" Gordon shouted, but we needn't have worried. The gas thief doubled over and began throwing up in the woods. Three uniformed police officers ran into our campsite and quickly apprehended the thief, who made no effort to get away. He was too busy throwing up. People in nearby trailers came over to see what the excitement was all about.

"These boys have caught the gas thief," announced one of the officers. "I don't know how you did it, but you managed to stop him in his tracks. I believe there's a reward waiting for you."

Later, after the commotion had died down and the other campers had drifted back to their own trailers, Gordon told us how he managed to catch the thief.

"It was simple," he said. He walked over to where the gas thief's siphon lay on the ground. "I just used a screw driver and switched these two signs," said Gordon, pointing to the trailer. Attached to the side of the trailer was a small metal sign that said "Gas", and right next to it was another small sign that said "Sewage." "The thief thought he was siphoning our gas, but what he was really doing was sucking in a mouthful of sewage from our washroom!"

"That's gross!" exclaimed Paulo. "But effective!"

"And brilliant!" I added.

"Not to mention that we have just earned ourselves $250.00!" said Gordon, and the three of us went inside the RV to figure out how we would spend our reward money.

Chapter 13
The Kidnapping

It was the end of summer, and for once, I couldn't wait to get back to school. My friends and I had been playing a prank on our teacher all summer long, and we were excited to see what her reaction was.

It was Gordon who had come up with the idea at the end of June, at our school's final assembly. Our teacher, Mrs. Hoagsbrith, had been presented with a gift for 25 years of teaching. She unwrapped the gift in front of the entire gymnasium filled with students. Apparently,

Mrs. Hoagsbrith loves gardening, and she has a large collection of garden gnomes. For her 25th anniversary of teaching, the school gave her an expensive pair of matching garden gnomes to add to her collection. As our teacher was making a speech and thanking everyone for the gnomes, Gordon shot me a look that I knew only too well.

Immediately after the assembly, Gordon pulled Paulo and me aside and said, "Guys, I just got the greatest idea!"

Paulo and I were used to Gordon's "great" ideas, and more than a few of them had landed us in big trouble.

"What is it this time?" asked Paulo warily.

"Well, you know those gnomes that the school gave Mrs. H.? Wouldn't it be funny if they got kidnapped?"

"What? We can't steal her new garden gnomes," I argued.

"I didn't say *steal*," replied Gordon. "I said, *kidnap*. We'll return them when we're done."

"When we're done *what?*" asked Paulo suspiciously.

"Oh, just taking them on vacation. Paulo, you're going

to Niagara Falls this summer, right? Wouldn't it be funny if Mrs. H. got a picture of her gnomes beside the falls?"

"That would be funny," I said. "And I'm going to the beach a week later. I could take the gnomes with me."

And so it was that our plan was born.

*   *   *

Two days later, Gordon and I slept over at Paulo's house. We set our alarm clock for 4:00 a.m. and while it was still dark outside, we snuck out of the house with pillowcases tucked under our arms, hopped on our bikes and pedalled to our teacher's house. We had been there last winter during a snowstorm, so we were sure we could find her house again.

"There it is!" I cried, pointing down the dirt road to an old farmhouse.

"Look at all the gnomes," said Paulo. "How will we know which ones are the new ones?"

"We have to look for a matching pair," said Gordon. "But hurry. It's starting to get light."

As planned, I got off my bike and pulled a pen and

notepad out of my pocket. I jotted down the name of the road and Mrs. Hoagsbrith's address. Next, I pulled the note we had written out of my pocket and ran up to the front porch. I tucked the note in the screen door. In the meantime, Paulo and Gordon had dropped their bikes in the ditch and darted across the lawn. When they found what they were certain were the new gnomes, they threw their pillowcases over them and quickly carried them back to their bikes. The three of us took off down the road.

Later that morning, when Mrs. Hoagsbrith woke up, she would find a note in her front door that said:

> *Your gardens are lovely and we like living*
> *here, but we need a vacation.*
> *See you in September,*
> *Mr. & Mrs. Gnome*
> *P.S. We'll write to you.*

Gordon, Paulo and I spent the rest of the summer traveling with the gnomes tucked in our suitcases and backpacks. Whenever we could, we snuck the gnomes out and took their picture and sent it to our teacher. There were pictures of the gnomes in front of Niagara Falls. Paulo wrote, *"Having a wonderful time"* on the back of the picture and dropped it in the mail. I photographed the gnomes wearing sunglasses lying on a towel on the beach. *"Wish you were here," I* wrote on the back before mailing it off to our teacher. Gordon snapped a picture of the gnomes sitting on lawn chairs holding flags in front of a fireworks display. While visiting his Uncle Ivan, we took their picture sitting around the campfire toasting marshmallows on sticks. *"See you soon,"* was written on the back of the picture.

Two days before school was to begin, we made another early morning call to our teacher's house and snuck the garden gnomes onto the front porch where she would be sure to find them. Next to them we sat a tiny doll's suitcase that Gordon had borrowed from his little sister. Taped to one of the gnomes was a note that said, *"It's good to be home."*

* * *

On the first day of school, Gordon, Paulo and I waited all day to hear Mrs. Hoagsbrith tell everyone the story about her gnomes being kidnapped, but she didn't mention it. She said nothing about it the second or third day of school, either, and then it happened. On the fourth day, Gordon, Paulo and I overheard Mrs. Hoagsbrith talking to another teacher on yard duty.

"So, did you do anything exciting over the summer?" he asked her.

"No. It was a quiet summer," she said. "After last year, I just needed to relax. My next-door neighbour had some excitement, though. He collects garden gnomes, too, and he has an even larger collection than I do. Someone took two of his gnomes at the beginning of the summer and took pictures of them all over the country on vacation! It was pretty funny, and the gnomes were returned undamaged, but he has no idea who would pull such a stunt."

"Gordon!" I whispered. "We must have got the wrong house!"

"Oh, no!" said Paulo. "All that work for nothing. I guess the joke's on us."

Paulo and I swore that it was the last time we would ever let Gordon talk us into one of his great ideas.

About the Authors

Michael Wade was born a long time ago, in a place far, far away. He grew up in London, Ontario and currently lives in Strathroy, Ontario. Michael enjoys hunting, wilderness canoeing and working out.

Laura Wade was born not quite so long ago and not as far away as Michael. She, too, was raised in London, Ontario and currently resides in Strathroy, where she works as a Children's Librarian.